ONE OF
YOUR
LEGS
IS
BOTH
THE
SAME

One of Your Legs is Both the Same

Poems by
Adrian Henri
Terry Jones
Colin McNaughton
Michael Rosen
Kit Wright

Compiled by Eunice McMullen
Illustrated by Colin McNaughton

MACMILLAN
CHILDREN'S BOOKS

First published 1994 by Pan Macmillan Children's Books

This edition published 1995 by Macmillan Children's Books
a division of Macmillan Publishers Limited
25 Eccleston Place London SW1W 9NF
and Basingstoke

Associated companies throughout the world

ISBN: 0 330 32704 6

3 5 7 9 8 6 4

A CIP catalogue record for this book is available from
the British Library

Printed and bound in Great Britain by
Mackays of Chatham PLC, Chatham, Kent

Contents

One of Your Legs is Both the Same

Your hair's all over the top of your head.
What are you doing here? What's your game?
Your boots are on two different feet
And one of your legs is both the same.

Look at your mouth: it's full of teeth.
Where did you come from? What's your name?
Have you seen your knees? They're wearing caps
And one of your legs is both the same.

A couple of holes at the end of your nose:
What is the reason? Who's to blame?
Each of your ears is the right way round
And one of your legs is both the same.

Your fingers are fixed at the end of your hands.
Haven't you got any sense of shame?
Your head's stuck right on top of your neck
And one of your legs is both the same.

K.W.

Mrs Mather

Scared stiff.
Courage flown.
On that doorstep all alone.
Cold sweat.
State of shock.
Lift my trembling hand and knock.

Thumping heart.
Chilled with fear.
I hear the witch's feet draw near.
Rasping bolts.
Rusty locks.
Shake down to my cotton socks.

Hinges creaking.
Waft of mould.
A groan that makes my blood run cold.
Cracking voice.
Knocking knees.
'Can I have my ball back, please?'

C.M^CN.

Rodge

Rodge said,
'Teachers – they want it all ways –
You're jumping up and down on a chair
or something
and they grab hold of you and say,
"Would you do that sort of thing in your own
home?" '

   'So you say, "No."
   And they say,
   "Well don't do it here then." '

'But if you say, "Yes, I do it at home."
they say,
"Well, we don't want that sort of thing
going on here
thank you very much." '

   'Teachers – they get you all ways,'
   Rodge said.

M.R.

Pool Players

Some say
Ullapool's
a duller pool
than Liverpool
but give a pool
a chance!

I say
Ullapool's
a filled-with-life-
and-colour pool
where people sing
and dance.

Some say
Hartlepool's
an only-just-
and-partly pool
but give a pool
a break!

I say
Hartlepool's
a look-alive-
and-smartly pool
where folk are wide
awake.

As every Hartlepudlian
and every Ullapudlian
and every Liverpudlian

knows, for heaven's sake!

K.W.

The Lion's Den

'Bring all your pets in tomorrow,
We'll all have a jolly nice time.'
To teacher, a pet means a gerbil;
She obviously hasn't seen mine!

C.M^cN.

If All the Stars in Heaven

If all the stars in heaven
Were made of Katto-meat,
I bet our cat would still make out
He'd not enough to eat!

If I were filled with rubbish,
And all I spoke was birds,
I'd never eat my heart out
– Though I might eat my words.

T.J.

Simple Simon

Simple Simon met a pieman
Going to the fair;
Said Simple Simon to the pieman
'What have you got there?'
Said the pieman to Simple Simon
'I've got a load of pies.'
Said Simple Simon to the pieman
'Ugh – they're all covered in flies.'

M.R.

I'm Much Better than You

My dad's bigger than your dad,
Got more money too.
My house is posher than your house –
I'm much better than you.

My mum's prettier than your mum,
Our car is faster too.
We have a house in the country –
I'm much better than you.

My toys cost more than your toys,
My clothes are trendier too.
My school costs more than your school –
I'm much better than you.

We have a maid and a nanny,
We have a gardener too.
I'm driven to school by our chauffeur –
I'm much better than you.

Our summers we spend in Tahiti,
In winter we ski in Peru.
My cousin Di's married royalty –
I'm much better than . . .

At this point the poem comes to a terrible end when an armed and extremely dangerous grizzly bear, *Ursus horribilis*, who is on the run from the maximum security wing of London Zoo and who has not eaten for three days, leaps from behind a tree and swallows up the boy without so much as a 'How do you do?' – sad, eh?

C.M^cN.

Ranzo

Who rolled in the mud
behind the garage door?
Who left footprints
across the kitchen floor?

I know a dog whose nose is cold
I know a dog whose nose is cold

Who chased raindrops
down the windows?
Who smudged the glass
with the end of his nose?

I know a dog with a cold in his nose
I know a dog with a cold in his nose

Who wants a bath
and a big crunchy biscuit?
Who wants to bed down
in his fireside basket?

Me, said Ranzo
I'm the dog with a cold.

M.R.

Said the Boy to the Dinosaur

Said the boy to the dinosaur:
  'Outa my way!'
Said the dinosaur:
  'That's not a nice thing to say.'

Said the boy to the dinosaur:
  'Go take a hike!'
Said the dinosaur:
  'Not an expression I like.'

Said the boy to the dinosaur:
  'Move aside Mac!'
Said the dinosaur:
  'Obviously, manners you lack.'

Said the boy to the dinosaur:
  'Go fly a kite!'
Said the dinosaur:
  'That's what I call impolite.'

Said the boy to the dinosaur:
  'Jump in the lake!'
Said the dinosaur:
  'That is as much as I'll take!'

The monster was cross,
   Which is what you'd expect;
'I'm older than you,
   You should show some respect!'

He taught him a lesson,
   What more can I say?
The dinosaur ate him
   And went on his way.

C.M^cN.

Give Up Slimming Mum

My Mum
is short
and plump
and pretty
and I wish
she'd give up
slimming.

So does Dad.

Her cooking's
delicious –
you can't
beat it –
but you really can
hardly bear
to eat it –
that way she sits
with her eyes

brimming,
watching you
polish off
the spuds
and trimmings
while she
has nothing
herself but a small
thin dry
diet biscuit:
that's all.

My Mum
is short
and plump
and pretty
and I wish
she'd give up
slimming.

So does Dad.

She says she
looks as though
someone had
sat on her –
BUT WE LIKE MUM
WITH A BIT
OF FAT ON HER!

K.W.

Horace

Much to his Mum and Dad's dismay
Horace ate himself one day.
He didn't stop to say his grace,
He just sat down and ate his face.
'We can't have this!' his Dad declared,
'If that lad's ate, he should be shared.'
But even as he spoke they saw
Horace eating more and more:
First his legs, and then his thighs,
His arms, his nose, his hair, his eyes . . .
'Stop him, someone!' Mother cried,
'Those eyeballs would be better fried!'
But all too late! And now the silly
Had even started on his willy!
'Oh foolish child!' the father mourns,
'You could have deep-fried that with prawns,
Some parsley and some tartare sauce . . .'
But H. was on his second course:
His liver and his lights and lung,
His ears, his neck, his chin, his tongue . . .
'To think I raised him from the cot,
And now he's going to scoff the lot!'
His Mother cried, 'What shall we do?
What's left won't even make a stew!'

And as she wept, her son was seen
To eat his head, his heart, his spleen.
And there he lay – a boy no more –
Just a stomach on the floor . . .
But none the less, since it *was* his,
They ate it – that's what haggis is.*

T.J.

*No it isn't. Haggis is a kind of stuffed pudding eaten by the Scots.
The minced heart, liver, lungs of a sheep, calf or other animal's
inner organs are mixed with oatmeal, sealed and boiled in the maw
(in the stomach-bag) of a sheep and . . . excuse me a minute. *Ed.*

Potty

Don't put that potty on your head, Tim.
Don't put that potty on your head.
  It's not very clean
  And you don't know where it's been,
So don't put that potty on your head.

C.M^cN.

Poor Little Arabella

Poor Little Arabella,
Why didn't someone tell her
Not to use her umbrella
When the north wind blows?

C.M^cN.

Me and My Brother

Me and my brother,
we sit up in bed
doing my dad's sayings.
I go to bed first
and I'm just dozing off
and I hear a funny voice going:
'Never let me see you doing that again,'
and it's my brother
poking his finger out just like my dad
going:
'Never let me see you doing that again.'
And so I join in
and we're both going:

'Never
let
me
see
you
doing
that
again.'

So what happens next time I get into trouble
and my dad's telling me off?
He's going:
'Never let me see you doing that again.'
So I'm looking up at my dad
going,
'Sorry, Dad, sorry,'

and I suddenly catch sight of my brother's big red
face poking out from behind my dad.

And while my dad is poking me with his finger
in time with the words:
'Never
let
me
see
you
doing
that again,'
there's my brother doing just the same
behind my dad's back
just where I can see him
and he's saying the words as well
with his mouth without making a sound.

So I start laughing
and so my dad says,
'AND IT'S NO LAUGHING MATTER.'
Of course my brother knows that one as well
and he's going with his mouth:
'And it's no laughing matter.'

But my dad's not stupid.
He knows something's going on.
So he looks round
and there's my brother
with his finger poking out
just like my dad
and I'm standing there laughing.
Oh no
then we get into
REALLY BIG TROUBLE.

M.R.

The Day the Animals Talked

I woke up one morning
When the sun was high,
And I thought: 'Something's up!'
Though I didn't know why.

I got out of bed,
Then I went white as chalk,
For I suddenly heard
My goldfish talk.

'Ah! You've got up at last!
And about time!' it said.
'I've been swimming all night,
While you've been in bed!'

Well! You can imagine
My utter surprise;
I didn't believe
My ears or my eyes.

I was going to exclaim:
'Did *I* hear *you* talk?'
But just then the dog said:
'I need a walk!'

I turned and saw Rover
(Imagine the shock)
As he said: 'A good long one –
Not once round the block!'

I thought: 'This is crazy!'
But more was to come . . .
When I started to answer,
I found I was dumb!

I spluttered and pointed
And tried to say: 'Wait!'
But nothing came out,
And the cat muttered: 'Great!

'The Boss has gone mute on us!
Just what we need!
How's he going to buy catfood?'
'And what about seed?'

This was the budgie,
Pacing its cage,
And who all of a sudden
Flew into a rage:

'Lemme out! You sadist!'
It pecked at its bell.
'I can't bear this prison!
My life here is hell!'

I tried to say 'Sorry!'
But nothing came out,
Then it was the goldfish
Who'd started to shout:

'What about me?
I'm stuck in this bowl
With nowhere to hide
Not so much as a hole!

'Don't you think *I* go crazy?
I'm stared at all day
By that monster!' But Ginger
The cat looked away.

And I tried to say: 'Pets!
Please listen to me!'
But I was as dumb
As *they'd* been previously.

'You listen to us,
For a change!' said a mouse
Who appeared on a cupboard
'We live in this house,

'Yet you fill it with traps,
And you poison my young!'
And the others all murmured:
'He ought to be hung!'

But Rover stood by me,
And said: 'Listen here!
It may be the Master
Has just no idea

'Of half of the things
That go on in his name . . .'
The cat said: 'Let's show him!'
The rest said: 'We're game!'

So the animals dragged me
By beak and by paw
To the zoo, and I couldn't
Believe what I saw:

All the cages were open
The creatures roamed free,
And walked on their hind legs
Like you and like me.

When they saw me, they started
To scream: 'One's got loose!'
'That's a dangerous animal!'
Clamoured a goose.

'They've cooked all my ancestors,
Thousands a year!'
'And mine!' cried a bison.
'And mine!' sighed a deer.

And the animals started
To bellow and roar,
Till the lion held up
An immaculate paw:

'Now listen! A lot of us
Hunt for our meat.
This creature's no different.
His kind have to eat.'

'But they torture us, Lion!'
The goose again crowed.
'They force us to feed
Till our livers explode!'

'Is this *possible*, Man?'
The lion turned to me,
And I couldn't deny it
(Nor could I agree).

And the murmur of horror
Turned into a roar,
As the leopard sprang up
And growled: 'I hate him more!

'At least the Man eats
The geese that he kills –
My kind he pursues
For his fashions and frills!'

'That's right!' cried the mink
And the seals and the bears.
'Who wants to be murdered
For something *he* wears?'

'And us, dears!' the musk deer
Were whispering as well.
'We're slaughtered merely
Cause men like our smell!'

'Ah! My friends! This is nothing!'
The fox had begun,
'Men hunt us poor foxes
Simply for *fun*!'

The babble of voices
Arose to the skies,
And the lion turned to me
With tears in his eyes.

'Oh, Man!' he said sadly,
'What have you to say?'
And I stood there as dumb
As a bottle of hay.

'Make him into a hand-bag!'
The crocodiles croaked.
'Turn him into a hat-stand,'
The elephants joked.

Hand-bag!

And the lion said: 'Oh, Man!
How *could* you have done
All these terrible things
By the light of the sun?

'You're found to be guilty!
You have no excuse,
And your punishment shall
Be pronounced by the goose!'

Then the animals bickered
And cried: 'No! Let me!'
But the goose cackled: 'Listen!
Here's what it shall be!

'Let's leave him to stew
On his own for a bit,
Then we'll pluck him and gut him
To roast on the spit!'

But the rest started screeching
With different ideas,
And I dropped to my knees,
With my hands on my ears.

Then I felt myself lifted
And thrown in a cage
And I lay there in terror
For what seemed an age . . .

I awoke all alone.
Above me – the stars –
When I suddenly heard
A quiet tap on the bars,

And there was old Rover
At my cage's doors,
Concern in his eyes
And a key in his jaws.

'Come on, Master,' he grumbled,
'While everyone sleeps,
Let's get out of here
– this place gives me the creeps!'

He opened the cage
And I licked his dear face,
And I kept close to heel,
For I felt in disgrace.

And when we got home
He put me to bed
Under the table,
and gently he said:

'Goodnight, old fellow,'
In his kindly tone,
And he patted my head,
And he gave me a bone.

And I settled right down,
And I slept like a log,
Thinking: 'Golly! I'm happy
I'm only a dog!'

T.J.

Tickle

When I tickle Laura on the back of her neck
she snorts and cackles
and giggles and gargles
and wheezes
her face creases up
she looks like she's going to burst
until she shouts:
NO MORE DADDO
NO MORE DADDO.

Everything goes quiet.

Then she says:

M.R.

more kickle now Daddo!

Ghosts

That's right. Sit down and talk to me.
What do you want to talk about?

Ghosts. You were saying that you believe in them.
Yes, they exist, without a doubt.

What, bony white nightmares that rattle and glow?
No, just spirits that come and go.

I've never heard such a load of rubbish.
Never mind, one day you'll know.

What makes you so sure?

I said:
What makes you so sure?

Hey,
Where did you go?

K.W.

The Car Trip

Mum says:
'Right, you two,
this is a very long car journey.
I want you two to be good.
I'm driving and I can't drive properly
if you two are going mad in the back.
Do you understand?'

So we say,
OK, Mum, OK. Don't worry,
and off we go.

And we start The Moaning:
Can I have a drink?
I want some crisps.
Can I open my window?
He's got my book.
Get off me.
Ow, that's my ear!

And Mum tries to be exciting:
'Look out the window
there's a lamp-post.'

And we go on with The Moaning:
Can I have a sweet?
He's sitting on me.
Are we nearly there?
Don't scratch.

You never tell him off.
Now he's biting his nails.
I want a drink. I want a drink.

And Mum tries to be exciting again:
'Look out the window
There's a tree.'

And we go on:
My hands are sticky.
He's playing with the doorhandle now.
I feel sick.
Your nose is all runny.
Don't pull my hair.
He's punching me, Mum,
that's really dangerous, you know.
Mum, he's spitting.

And Mum says:
'Right I'm stopping the car.
I AM STOPPING THE CAR.'

She stops the car.

'Now, if you two don't stop it
I'm going to put you out of the car
and leave you by the side of the road.'

He started it.
I didn't. He started it.

'I don't care who started it
I can't drive properly
if you two go mad in the back.
Do you understand?'

And we say:
OK Mum, OK, don't worry.

Can I have a drink?

M.R.

Adios Amigos . . .

¡THE MEXICANS ARE COMING!
The whisper goes round the school
persistent as the smell of garlic.
Strange sounds come from the kitchens,
Mariachi Bands and maracas,
Shouts of 'Olé'. They're going crackers.

¡THE MEXICANS ARE HERE!
Rumour spreads, hot as chili-powder.
The dinner-ladies burst through the kitchen door
clapping their hands, stamping their heels on the floor.
Brightly-coloured shawls swirl. Boys and girls
watch, wide-eyed as a bullfight crowd.

¡THE MEXICANS HAVE COME!
Michelle's Mum serves Tropical Dessert
with a flick of her skirt. Her friends serve
Chile con Chips, Baked Beans y Tortillas
wearing black lace mantillas. It tastes
really nice, and it's just the same price.

¡THE MEXICANS HAVE BEEN!
They haven't been seen for days. Just aprons of green
and the clatter of trays. Distant as holidays
and a tropical moon. I hope they come back soon.
The Headmaster's put his sombrero away.
Cos nothing's the same since that wonderful day
when all cried 'Olé',

                    when the Mexicans came . . .

                                        A.H.

43

Bill's Eraser

Bill had an eraser
That was better than you think:
It could rub out almost anything
From pencil marks to ink.
It could even rub out paint-marks,
Biro, felt-tip, crayon, glue!
And that is just the start of what
That crazy thing could do.
It could rub out paper
And erase whole books – no fool!
It could rub the desk and table out –
It could even rub out school!
'Stop it!' cried his Teacher,
As he rubbed *her* out one day.
'You're not allowed to use that . . .' But
That's all she'd time to say!
And he erased the masters
Who came running to her aid.
He erased the Police Inspector.
He erased the Fire Brigade.

So then they sent the Army in
With guns and armoured tanks,
And a Colonel yelled: 'Surrender!'
To which Bill replied: 'No thanks!'
And he just erased their bullets
When the men began to shoot,
And then he rubbed the Colonel out –
From cap to polished boot.
Then he erased a tank or two,
Till someone cried: 'Ceasefire!'
And all the soldiers round the school
Hastened to retire.
But Bill just ran ahead of them
And he erased the street
So there was nowhere they could go,
And they called out: 'You cheat!'
But still Bill hadn't finished,
And they couldn't fire a shot
Before he'd got amongst them,
And just erased the lot!

Then Bill felt rather hungry,
And, looking round, he saw
A locked-up supermarket –
So he erased the door,
And went in and ate everything
He liked on every shelf.
Then feeling full, and rather sick,
Young Bill erased himself!

As
   he
      did
         the world went grey
And then completely white.
He thought he could hear voices
To his left and to his right,
But nothing there was visible
In that Erasered World –
Just whiteness, and all around him now
A sea of noises swirled.

There were gunshots there and shouting,
And he heard his Teacher sigh:
'Where are we all? What can we do?'
Then she began to cry.
Then he heard some masters talk
One said: 'I'll never see
Form 3 again. I wonder if
Those blighters will miss *me*?'
'I should be taking Latin now,'
Another said: 'Just think!'
And Mr Williamson, the Head,
Said: 'Cor! I need a drink!'
And then Bill heard the Police Inspector
Choking back his tears;
'I'd just got married yesterday . . .
We'd been engaged eight years!'
'I'll never see my daughter,'
Said a fireman, 'or my son!'
And Bill said to himself: 'Oh dear!
Whatever have I done?

'I guess I never realised
Adults could get so gloomy
I thought they just liked getting cross
And threatening to do me.'
'It's him!' exclaimed the Colonel.
'Attack! Let's get him, men!'
But in that whiteness all he heard
Was: 'Who?' 'What?' 'Where?' 'How?' 'When?'

There was suddenly confusion
And the artillery began,
Until Bill shouted out: 'No! Wait!
I think I've got a plan!'
'What's that, Bill?' asked his Teacher,
When the Army had quite done.
Whereupon Bill got a pencil out
And drew round everyone.
He drew their hands and arms and heads.
He shaded in their hair,
And then he gave them legs and feet,
And drew them clothes to wear.

But when he'd finished, most of them
Said: 'Oy! We don't look right!'
And, as Bill's drawing wasn't great,
They did look quite a sight!

'I want a better face than this!'
The Gym Mistress complained.
'And *I* need a proper uniform,'
The Colonel looked quite pained.
'I just don't look like *anything*,'
The Police Inspector said.
'And I look like a drunken slob!'
Moaned Mr Williamson, the Head.
'At least we all can see ourselves,'
Bill's Teacher smiled, then she
Said: 'Now the problem's getting back
Into Reality.'
'How on Earth can we do that?'
Said the Fire Chief, looking cross,
And everybody scratched their heads,
And just seemed at a loss.

At length, his Teacher turned to Bill,
And said: 'It's up to you.
You got us in this mess –
What do *you* intend to do?'
Bill looked around his drawings
In that Limbo World of White,
And then he cried: 'I've got it!'
And he gripped his pencil tight.

Then he drew a wobbly staircase
Rising up beside a sea,
And he started to climb up it
Yelling back: 'Now follow me!'

Well, as they all ascended,
Bill drew the staircase on,
Until at last it ended
In a sort of Parthenon.
And then he drew a sort of lump
(It wasn't awfully clear)
And all his teachers looked at Bill
And muttered: 'Dear oh dear!'

The Colonel got real angry
And said: 'What's *that*, you silly clod?'
At which Bill's drawing rose and said:
'Why! Can't you tell? I'm God.'

For a moment everyone seemed stunned,
Then they dropped upon their knees,
And mumbled: 'Oh! Forgive us, Lord!'
And: 'Don't be wrathful, *please*!'
But God seemed pretty cheerful,
And said: 'Why have you drawn me?'
And Bill replied: 'Please get us back
Into Reality.'

The Heretofore

So God took up Bill's pencil,
And he drew a marvellous door,
With a polished brass plate on it
Which read: 'THE HERETOFORE'.
Then God just gave a chuckle,
'Right! In you go!' he said,
And everyone piled through and found . . .

. . . They were back home in bed.

Next day at school, Bill learnt that things
Are – sometimes – what they seem,
For everyone he met had had
This very self-same dream.
And when he realised what he'd done –
How lucky he'd been too –
He swore he'd try and look at things
From others' points-of-view.

Bill's still got his eraser,
But he's never told his mates,
And he only rubs out pencil marks
And not the things he hates.

T.J.

Paracetamol
for Spike Sterne

If a giraffe has a headache
Or a chimpanzee has a fall
There's no aspirins in the jungle
'Cause the parrots ate 'em all.

A.H.

Tall Story

I went to the theatre to cheer myself up,
I was hoping to have a few laughs.
   But I found, don't you know,
   The entire front row,
Had been booked by a bunch of giraffes!

C.M^cN.

I'm Carrying the Baby

Paul was three.
'Look at me,' he said,
'look at me
I'm carrying the baby
look at me
look at me
I'm carrying the baby.'

'Oh,' said Paul,
'look at me
I've dropped the baby.'

M.R.

Wardrobe

I've got nothing to wear!
There isn't a thing there
that will do.
It's true: the only good things
aren't clean. And these jeans
are no use. It's not an excuse;
I couldn't go out in *that*:
I'd look like something the cat
had dragged in. Most of this
is only fit for the bin.
I don't know where to begin.
I'd go out and buy something new
except I've got nothing to go in.
I don't know what to do.

Of course! Why didn't I think of it before?
I'll borrow something off you . . .

A.H.

Nightmare

I'm down
I'm underground

I'm down the Underground

Waiting

Waiting for a train

There's the platform
There's the lines
There's the tunnel
There's the lines.

I'll wait down there
Down between the lines
Waiting for the train
Down between the lines.
I'll climb down there
Down between the lines
and wait for the train
down there.

Look

Look up the tunnel look
Yes it's coming, it's coming
they say,
And it is.
And I'm between the lines.

And I can see it
See it coming
and I'm between the lines.

Can someone give me a
hand up?
Can't you see?

I'm between the lines
and the train's coming.
Can't you see?

I'm between the lines
and the train's coming.
Give me a hand someone
give me a hand
the train's coming
give me a hand
I can't climb up.
The train's coming
and the platform's sliding in
towards me too
with the train still coming
coming down the tunnel
the platform's sliding
sliding in towards me too.

I'm still down
Can't anyone see me
down between the lines?

Look
see
me
the train
platform
me
the train
near now
nearer now
nearer and nearer now
NOW

That's all.

M.R.

Animal Form

When you come to think of it,
And I do,
We're all a bunch of animals
In Class 2.

Annabel is baa-ing
Like a very old sheep.
Timothy's a dormouse,
Fast asleep.

Dilip and Philip
In one of their spats
Yowl at each other like
Two tom-cats.

Wayne is craning
Like a tall giraffe
Round Neeta's bunches
And her hyena laugh.

Josephine's a parrot,
Repeating what you say,
And Mrs Ford's a donkey
With her

All

Day

Bray!

K.W.

Nutter

The moon's a big white football,
The sun's a pound of butter.
The earth is going round the twist
And I'm a little nutter!

K.W.

Biology

The cell laughed as it split in two.
It thought that to divide itself
Was just the funniest thing to do –
And soon it was beside itself!

K.W.

Watch Your French

When my mum tipped a panful of red-hot fat
Over her foot, she did quite a little chat,
And I won't tell you what she said
But it wasn't:
'Fancy that!
I must try in future to be far more careful
With this red-hot scalding fat!'

When my dad fell over and landed – splat! –
With a trayful of drinks (he'd tripped over the cat)
I won't tell you what he said
But it wasn't:
'Fancy that!
I must try in future to be far more careful
To step *round* our splendid cat!'

When Uncle Joe brought me a cowboy hat
Back from the States, the dog stomped it flat,
And I won't tell you what I said
But Mum and Dad yelled:
'STOP THAT!
Where did you learn that appalling language?
Come on. Where?'

'I've no idea,' I said,
'No idea.'

K.W.

Mum is Having a Baby!

Mum is having a baby!
  I'm shocked! I'm all at sea!
What's she want another one for:
  WHAT'S THE MATTER WITH ME!?

C.M^CN.

Best Friends

It's Susan I talk to not Tracey,
Before that I sat next to Jane;
I used to be best friends with Lynda
But these days I think she's a pain.

Natasha's all right in small doses,
I meet Mandy sometimes in town;
I'm jealous of Annabel's pony
And I don't like Nicola's frown.

I used to go skating with Catherine,
Before that I went there with Ruth;
And Kate's so much better at trampoline:
She's a showoff, to tell you the truth.

I think that I'm going off Susan,
She borrowed my comb yesterday;
I *think* I might sit next to Tracey,
She's my nearly best friend: she's OK.

A.H.

Poem for a Little Prince

Away in a Palace, no crib for *his* bed,
The little Prince Henry lays down his sweet head;
A radiant mother and servants in rows,
Detectives to follow wherever he goes.

The cameras are whirring, the baby awakes,
But little Prince Henry no crying he makes:
No magical kiss and no dragons to slay,
Young Harry will marry a Princess one day.

A.H.

Permit Holders Only

Daddy had an argument on Friday night,
With a man from outer space.
Daddy said, 'I don't care where you're from,
You're in my parking place!'

C.M^cN.

Nightmare Cemetery

Don't go down with me today
to Nightmare Cemetery
You don't know what you'll see today
in Nightmare Cemetery

Don't go through the gates today
to Nightmare Cemetery
You don't know what waits today
in Nightmare Cemetery

Don't go down the lane today
to Nightmare Cemetery
There you might remain today
in Nightmare Cemetery

Don't go down the road today
to Nightmare Cemetery
Haunt of bat and toad today
in Nightmare Cemetery

The sun will never shine today
in Nightmare Cemetery
Horrors wait in line today
in Nightmare Cemetery

Close the gates and step inside
Much too late to try and hide
Hear the hinges creak with glee
I'll be waiting, just you see,
You're here forever, just like me
in Nightmare Cemetery.

A.H.

Kate

I think I'm in love with Kate
it can't just be her dimples
it's not as simple
as that.

Shirley's blonde and Sue's hair's red
and curly. But I like dark hair
short and straight
like Kate.

I think that I'm too late.
She'll go straight home. Perhaps
she'll wait and say
'Hello'.

I'll walk home past her street.
Perhaps I'll meet her on the way.
I won't know what
to say.

I pulled her hair and called her names today.
She ran away. I'm *sure* she knows
that I'm in love
with Kate.

A.H.

Square Meal

He kept a pet hyena
And then he bought a flock
He fed them all on Oxo cubes
And made a laughing stock.

A.H.

Manners

'Finbar, do you want some soup?'
Said Finbar's mother when he was two.
'No.' 'Not no, *no thank you*, mummy,
Is what you say, you know you do.'

'Finbar, it's time to go to bed.'
'No thank you, mummy,' Finbar said.

K.W.

Book Day

'I must act sensibly'
Today's Book Day, you see.
A poet, an illustrator and a video.
Pinocchio. Or *The 39 Steps*
for the big ones. I had two helpings
of apple-pie and 100 lines.
'I must act sensibly'
What, me? Of course I was behaving,
just like they do in books.
I was strangling a boy
from 2c.

for the boys of Tonstall School

A.H.

Sick of Being Pushed Around?

Sick of being
Pushed around,
I sent away
For a course I'd found
In a Batman comic;
Only cost one pound.
It promised to make me
Musclebound.
I must say I quite
Like the sound
Of a powerful body
That would astound!

They sent part one,
My arms look great!
Part two is 'Legs' –
I just can't wait!

C.M^cN.

Autumn

Season of conkers and fireworks
and mellow fruitfulness. New shoes,
and a coat that's a bit too big,
to grow into next year. Blackberries
along the canal, white jungles
of frost on the window. Leaves
to kick all the way home,
the smell of bonfires,
stamping the ice on puddles
into crazy-paving. The nights come in
early, and you can't play out
after school. Soon
there'll be tangerines in the shops,
in shiny paper like Christmas-lights.

The little ones write letters to Santa Claus.

The big ones laugh under the streetlights.

A.H.

A Poem for my Cat

You're black and sleek and beautiful
What a pity your best friends won't tell you
Your breath smells of Kit-E-Kat.

A.H.

The Weather Never Bothers Me

I went to see my friend today,
To see if he'd come out to play.
He said, 'No fear, you must be mad,
I'm staying at home with Mum and Dad!
It's freezing cold – it's minus three!'
He slammed the door and turned the key.
I'm mystified, I'm all at sea,
He's soft as clarts – he has to be.
The weather never bothers me!

C.M^cN.

The Dark

I don't like the dark coming down on my head
It feels like a blanket thrown over the bed
I don't like the dark coming down on my head

I don't like the dark coming down over me
It feels like the room's full of things I can't see
I don't like the dark coming down over me

There isn't enough light from under the door
It only just reaches the edge of the floor
There isn't enough light from under the door

I wish that my dad hadn't put out the light
It feels like there's something that's just out of sight
I wish that my dad hadn't put out the light

But under the bedclothes it's warm and secure
You can't see the ceiling you can't see the floor
Yes, under the bedclothes it's warm and secure
So I think I'll stay here till it's daylight once more.

A.H.

Dunce

I always try my hardest,
  I always do my best.
It's just that I don't seem to be
  As clever as the rest.

C.M^cN.

Blue Christmas

I'm having a lousy Christmas
Not even a robin in sight,
There's a great big hole in my stocking,
and I've just fused the Christmas tree lights.

The dog is away in the manger,
Even the pudding won't light;
Singing Merry Christmas
On this all-too-silent night.

Good King Wenceslas looked out
Over a year ago:
How can I follow his footsteps
Where there isn't any snow?

The mistletoe's getting all dusty
With no one there to kiss,
Even the mince pies taste musty:
Can New Year be worse than this?

A.H.

I've Seen a Snowman Fly!

I've seen a snowman fly,
I have,
I've seen a snowman fly!
I saw it and I ain't mistook,
It wasn't in a picture book:
The snowman stood there, frozen stiff
And I just pushed him off the cliff!
I've seen a snowman fly,
I have,
I've seen a snowman fly.

C.M^cN.

Mm?

I say:
What are you doing? And our little boy Joe says,
Mm?
What d'you think you're doing?
Mm?
And why did you do that?
Mm?
The peanut butter. All over your blanket.
Mm?
And the talcum powder?
Mm?
Don't do it – do you understand?
Mm?
Or there'll be trouble. And Joe says,
Trouble,
and runs off laughing.

M.R.

Me

My Mum is on a diet,
My Dad is on the booze,
My Gran's out playing Bingo
And she was born to lose.

My brother's stripped his motorbike
Although it's bound to rain.
My sister's playing Elton John
Over and over again.

What a dim old family!
What a dreary lot!
Sometimes I think that I'm the only
Superstar they've got.

K.W.

Round the Park

Where are you going?
  Round the park
When are you back?
  After dark

Won't you be scared?
  What a laugh
A ghost'll get you
  Don't be daft

I know where it lives
  No you don't
And you'll run away
  No I won't

It got me once
  It didn't ... did it?
It's all SLIMY
  Tisn't ... is it?

Where are you going?
  I'm staying at home
Aren't you going to the park?
  Not on my own.

M.R.

Stew as Your Told

Wipe that face off your smile.
How many tunes do I have to tell you?
Don't eat with your mouthful.
When you cough, put your ear over your mouth.
Don't bite your nose.
Don't talk while I'm interrupting.

M.R.

INDEX OF AUTHORS
AND
FIRST LINES

Kit Wright

About the POETS

Adrian Henri

Adrian Henri was born in Birkenhead, across the River Mersey from Liverpool, was brought up in north Wales, didn't like poetry at school, and never wanted to be a poet. He was good at drawing and painting, and studied them at Newcastle University; he taught art, and eventually ended up back in Liverpool, where he still lives, and found to his surprise he'd turned into a poet. He's been publishing books of poetry for grown-ups since 1967, and writing for children, which is much more fun, since 1980. These include *Erik the Punk Cat* (1980) and *The Postman's Palace* (1990); his books of poems are *The Phantom Lollipop Lady* (1986), *Rhinestone Rhino* (1989), *Box* (1990), and *Dinner With the Spratts* (1993).

When he's not writing or painting, giving poetry readings or visiting schools he likes reading and watching TV, horror movies and Liverpool F.C.

Terry Jones

Terry Jones was born in Colwyn Bay, north Wales. He began writing at the age of seven and hasn't stopped since – both writing and performing comedy. A member of the Monty Python team, he has directed five feature films and written several books including *The Saga of Erik the Viking*, and also plays, films and TV scripts.

When asked 'Where *do* you get your ideas from?', he replies, 'From a little glass jar I found at the bottom of the garden. I think it must have been left by the fairies.'

Colin McNaughton

I was born in the north-east of England at an extraordinarily early age. In fact, legend has it I was born at the age of nought. I was always treated as a special child. Some point out this was because by the age of two I was six feet tall and could speak sixteen languages backwards. (Unfortunately, I couldn't speak any of them forwards.)

My early dreams of playing centre forward for Newcastle United were cruelly dashed when, at the age of six, I was turned down by the then manager Mr Joe 'bring 'im down!' Plankton. He said my footballing skills were wonderful but, because I was still talking backwards at this time, I failed the oral test. My attempts at common football phrases came out as '. Saint, game old funny a It's' and '. halves two of game a Football's'.

Brushing this disappointment aside I ran away to sea and joined a pirate ship called the *Golden Behind* as a cabin boy. However, Captain Abdul the Skinhead and his crew did not sail the Seven Seas they just sort of hung around the mouth of the River Tyne.

We did steal tons and tons of stuff, though: the Captain called it 'Black Gold', I called it 'coal'.

At the age of seven I travelled to London and got a job as Prime Minister, but was sacked for extending school summer holidays to fifty-one weeks plus one week for Christmas. Luckily, as I was removing my belongings from 10 Downing Street, a policeman stopped me and said, 'Colin, I hear there's a job going at Buckingham Palace. Why don't you apply for it?'

I started the next morning as Prince Philip, the Duke of Edinburgh. After opening several hospitals and sewage disposal works it was pointed out one day by a small boy that I looked nothing like Prince Philip (this was true). Once again I was unemployed. It was then I decided it was about time I had a proper education so, at the age of nine and a bit, I purchased an armadillo and enrolled at the Vinny Jones Academy of Verse and Drawing. The rest, as they say, is 'poetry'.

Michael Rosen

On first sight Michael
Rosen is largely loud
and hairy, hairily
large and loud and
loudly hairy and
large. When you get
to know him better
though, you find he's
just the same!

He has five
children, supports
Arsenal and likes
eating figgy rolls.

Kit Wright

Born south of the Medway river, Kit Wright is a true Kentish man whose passions (besides poetry) are trees, wild flowers, dogs, beer and cricket.

He writes poetry for children, grown-ups and anyone else who'll read them.

The title of his poem (and of this book) came to him in an inspired moment of creativity, but he's since been told that it is in fact the answer to the obvious question:

What's the difference between a duck?

One of its legs . . .

Acknowledgments

The compiler and publishers would like to thank the following for permission to reprint the selections in this book:

Rogers, Coleridge and White for 'Best Friends', 'Blue Christmas', 'Nightmare Cemetery', 'Poem for a Little Prince', 'A Poem for my Cat', and 'Square Meal' from *The Phantom Lollipop Lady* by Adrian Henri, published by Methuen Children's Books, © Adrian Henri 1986; and for 'Adios Amigos', 'The Dark', 'Kate' and 'Paracetamol' from *Rhinestone Rhino* by Adrian Henri, published by Methuen Children's Books, © Adrian Henri 1990.

Adrian Henri for 'Wardrobe', 'Book Day' and 'Autumn', © Adrian Henri 1992.

Pavilion Books for 'Bill's Eraser', 'The Day the Animals Talked', 'Horace' and 'If All the Stars in Heaven' from *The Curse of the Vampire's Socks* by Terry Jones, published by Pavilion Books, © Terry Jones 1988.

Walker Books for 'Dunce', 'I'm Much Better than You', 'Permit Holders Only', 'Poor Little Arabella' and 'Sick of Being Pushed Around' from *There's An Awful Lot of Weirdos in Our Neighbourhood* by Colin McNaughton, published by Walker Books, © Colin McNaughton 1987; for 'I've Seen a Snowman Fly!' and 'The Weather Never Bothers Me' from *Santa Clause is Superman* by Colin McNaughton, published by Walker Books, © Colin McNaughton 1988; and for 'The Lion's Den', 'Mum is Having a Baby!', 'Potty', 'Said the Boy to the Dinosaur', 'Scared Stiff' and 'Tall Story' from *Who's Been Sleeping in my Porridge?* by Colin McNaughton, published by Walker Books, © Colin McNaughton 1990.

Andre Deutsch Limited for 'I'm Carrying the Baby' and 'Nightmare' from *Don't Put Mustard in the Custard* by Michael Rosen, published by Andre Deutsch Limited, © Michael Rosen 1985; for 'Simple Simon' from *Hairy Tales and Nursery Crimes* by Michael Rosen, published by Andre Deutsch Limited, © Michael Rosen 1985; for 'Me and My Brother', 'Tickle' and 'The Car Trip' from *The Hypnotiser* by Michael Rosen, published by Andre Deutsch Limited, © Michael Rosen 1988; and for 'Ranzo' and 'Mm?' from *You Can't Catch Me* by Michael Rosen, published by Andre Deutsch Limited, © Michael Rosen 1981.

Penguin Books Ltd for 'Rodge' from *You Tell Me* by Roger McGough and Michael Rosen, published by Kestrel Books, © Michael Rosen 1979.

Michael Rosen for 'Stew as Your Told' and 'Round the Park', © Michael Rosen 1992.

HarperCollins Publishers Limited for 'Ghosts', 'Give Up Slimming Mum', 'Me', 'Nutter' and 'Watch Your French' from *Rabbiting On* by Kit Wright, published by HarperCollins Publishers Limited, © Kit Wright 1978.

Kit Wright for 'Animal Form', 'One of Your Legs is Both the Same', 'Pool Players', 'Manners' and 'Biology', © Kit Wright 1992.